P9-BBT-878

ONE MONDAY MORNING

ONE MONDAY MORNING

By Uri Shulevitz

Charles Scribner's Sons / New York

To Ehud

One Monday morning

the king,

the queen, and the little prince came to visit me.

But I wasn't home.

So the little prince said,
"In that case we shall return on Tuesday."

On Tuesday morning the king, the queen, the little prince,

and the knight came to visit me.

But I wasn't home.

So the little prince said,
"In that case we shall return on Wednesday."

On Wednesday morning
the king,
the queen,
the little prince,
the knight,
and a royal guard
came to visit me.

But I wasn't home.

So the little prince said,
"In that case we shall return on Thursday."

On Thursday morning
the king, the queen,
the little prince,
the knight, a royal guard,
and the royal cook
came to visit me.

But I wasn't home.

So the little prince said,
"In that case we shall return on Friday."

On Friday morning
the king, the queen,
the little prince,
the knight, the royal guard,
the royal cook,
and the royal barber
came to visit me.

But I wasn't home.

So the little prince said,
"In that case we shall return on Saturday."

5
FLOOR

On Saturday morning
the king, the queen,
the little prince,
the knight, a royal guard,
the royal cook,
the royal barber,
and the royal jester
came to visit me.

But I wasn't home.

So the little prince said,
"In that case we shall return on Sunday."

On Sunday morning the king, the queen,
the little prince, the knight, a royal guard,

the royal cook,
the royal barber,
the royal jester,
and a little dog
came to visit me.

And I was home.
So the little prince said,
"We just dropped in to say hello."

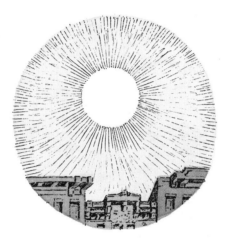

E   Shulevitz, Uri   *1496*
SHU
      One Monday morning

Mursis office 11/02

DATE			
FEB 18			
FEB 0 8 1993			
NOV. 02			
SEP. 1			

© THE BAKER & TAYLOR CO.